Red Hen

by Liza Charlesworth

ISBN: 978-1-338-84423-8

Art Director: Tannaz Fassihi; Designer: Cynthia Ng; Illustrated by Kevin Zimmer
Copyright © Liza Charlesworth. All rights reserved. Published by Scholastic Inc.

3 4 5 6 7   68   26 25 24

Printed in Jiaxing, China. First printing, June 2022.

■ SCHOLASTIC

Red Hen has a bus.
It is a hug bus!

Cub is sad.
But Red Hen
can fix it.

3

HUG!
Cub is not sad.
Cub is glad!

Did Cub get on
the hug bus?
Yes!

ug Bus

5

Pig is sad.
But Red Hen
can fix it.

HUG!
Pig is not sad.
Pig is glad!

Did Pig get on
the hug bus?
Yes!

Hug Bus

Ox is sad.
Sad, sad, sad.

But Red Hen, Cub,
and Pig can fix it.

HUG, HUG, HUG!
Ox is not sad.
Ox is GLAD.

Did Ox get on
the hug bus?
Yes!

12

The hug bus is
fun, fun, fun!

Read & Review

Invite your learner to point to each short-vowel word and read it aloud.

Short a

has
can
sad
glad

HUGS-R-US

Short e

yes
hen
red
get

14

Short i
fix
it
did
is
pig

Short o
ox
on
not
lot

Short u
bus
hug
but
cub
fun

g Bus

Fun Fill-Ins

Read the sentences aloud, inviting your learner to complete them using the short-vowel words in the box.

> Hen   it   sad   Ox   hug

1. The hug bus is driven by Red _____.
2. Red Hen sees that Cub is _____.
3. So Red Hen gives Cub a _____.
4. Red Hen, Cub, and Pig all give a hug to _____.
5. If you are sad, a hug can fix _____!